Verbal
Reasoning
Rapid Tests 2

Siân Goodspeed

Schofield&Sims

Introduction

This book gives you practice in answering verbal reasoning questions quickly.

The questions are like the questions on the 11+ and other school selection tests. You must find the correct answers.

School selection tests are usually timed, so you need to get used to working quickly. Each test has a target time for you to work towards. You should time how long you spend on each test, or you can ask an adult to time you.

What you need

- A pencil
- An eraser
- A clock, watch or stopwatch
- A sheet of rough paper
- An adult to help you work out how long you take and to mark the test for you

What to do

- Turn to **Section 1 Test 1** on page 4. Look at the grey box at the top of the page labelled **Target time**. This tells you how long the test should take.
- When you are ready to start, write down the time or start the stopwatch. Or the adult helping you will tell you to begin.
- Find this black arrow ⬇ near the top of the first page. Start each test here.
- Find this square ▦. The instructions for the first set of questions are beside it. Read them carefully.
- Look below the instructions. Read the **Example**. Work out why the answer given is correct.
- Use a similar method to answer question 1. Show your answer in the way that the answer is shown in the example. For instance, you might need to write your answer on the line or underline the correct answer from a selection given.
- Try to answer every question. If you do get stuck on a question, leave it and go on to the next one. Work quickly and try your best.
- Each test is one page long. When you reach the end, stop. Write down the time or stop the stopwatch. Or tell the adult that you have finished.
- With the adult, work out how long you took to do the test. Fill in the **Time taken** box at the end of the test.
- The adult will mark your test and fill in the **Score** and **Target met?** boxes.
- Turn to the **Progress chart** on page 40. Write your score in the box and colour in the graph to show how many questions you got right.
- Did you get some questions wrong? You should always have another go at them before you look at the answers. Then ask the adult to check your work and help you if you are still not sure.
- Later, you will do some more of these tests. You will soon learn to work through them more quickly. The adult who is helping you will tell you what to do next.

Published by **Schofield & Sims Ltd**,
7 Mariner Court, Wakefield, West Yorkshire WF4 3FL, UK
Telephone 01484 607080
www.schofieldandsims.co.uk
First published in 2014
This edition copyright © Schofield & Sims Ltd, 2018
Fourth impression 2021
Author: **Siân Goodspeed**. Siân Goodspeed has asserted her moral right under the Copyright, Designs and Patents Act, 1988, to be identified as the author of this work.
British Library Cataloguing in Publication Data. A catalogue record for this book is available from the British Library.

Commissioned by **Carolyn Richardson Publishing Services**

Design by **Oxford Designers & Illustrators**
Front cover design by **Ledgard Jepson Ltd**
Printed in the UK by **Page Bros (Norwich) Ltd**
ISBN 978 07217 1451 6

Contents

A **pull-out answers section** (pages A1 to A8) appears in the centre of this book, between pages 20 and 21. It also gives simple guidance on how best to use this book. Remove this section before the child begins working through the tests.

Underline the two words, **one** from each group, that mean almost the **same**.

Example (typical, <u>false</u>, halt)   (unusual, real, <u>untrue</u>)

1. (tired, grumpy, cheerful)   (sad, joyful, tried)
2. (rain, cloud, damp)   (dry, wet, towel)
3. (win, beat, team)   (hit, ball, hurt)

Choose the word that best completes the sentence. Underline the answer.

Example Music is to **listen** as **food** is to (touch, <u>taste</u>, drop).

4. **Sleep** is to **bedroom** as **cook** is to (eat, kitchen, stir).
5. **School** is to **teacher** as **hospital** is to (sick, doctor, ambulance).
6. **Cat** is to **meow** as **dog** is to (bark, quack, hoot).

Underline the two words, **one** from each group, that are most **opposite** in meaning.

Example (<u>after,</u> morning, begin)   (<u>before</u>, then, when)

7. (write, right, lift)   (left, draw, carry)
8. (cat, chair, sit)   (fell, stand, bend)
9. (wash, clean, bob)   (dirty, fork, sink)

Underline the word that goes best with the three words in brackets.

Example (wet, soaking, moist)   <u>damp</u>, swamp, rotten

10. (yellow, pink, blue)   green, sun, read
11. (van, lorry, truck)   road, lady, car
12. (mouse, frog, bird)   person, kangaroo, zoo

Score:		Time taken:		Target met?	

Target time: **12 minutes**

1–3. For each of the words below, choose the correct group. Write its letter on the line.

F = fish   **B** = bird

robin _____   owl _____

tuna _____   trout _____

cuckoo _____   cod _____

In each group, three words go together and one is the odd one out. Underline the word that does **not** go with the other three.

Example pound   <u>coin</u>   hit   thump

4. door   road   window   floor
5. field   branch   twig   leaf
6. car   lorry   driver   van

Underline the pair of words that are most **opposite** in meaning.

Example (begin, when)   (morning, then)   (<u>after, before</u>)

7. (race, sprint)   (jog, cross)   (quick, slow)
8. (rich, poor)   (paw, money)   (coin, spend)
9. (come, go)   (start, leaf)   (house, room)

Two words in each sentence must change places so that the sentence makes sense. Underline the two words.

Example I <u>a need</u> nap.   (I need a nap.)

10. The train fast is.

11. How many boats can see you?

12. My cat likes to milk drink.

Score:		Time taken:		Target met?	

Verbal Reasoning Rapid Tests 2   **5**

⬇

Underline the pair of words that mean almost the **same**.

Example (typical, unusual) (halt, real) (<u>false, untrue</u>)

1. (smart, clever)   (glass, plate)   (shiny, silly)
2. (hug, give)   (wind, story)   (finish, end)
3. (hungry, eat)   (drip, fat)   (slim, thin)

Choose the word that best completes the sentence. Underline the answer.

Example **Music** is to **listen** as **food** is to (touch, <u>taste</u>, drop).

4. **Right** is to **left** as **fast** is to (quick, rapid, slow).
5. **Yes** is to **no** as **wrong** is to (right, left, behind).
6. **Cat** is to **kitten** as **dog** is to (puppy, foal, lamb).

7–9. Look at these groups. For each of the words below, choose the correct group. Write its letter on the line.

A	B
lion	cow
tiger	sheep

giraffe _____   pig _____

duck _____   elephant _____

leopard _____   goat _____

In each group, three words go together and one is the odd one out. Underline the word that does **not** go with the other three.

Example pound   <u>coin</u>   hit   thump

10. petal   chair   leaf   stem

11. lion   tiger   leopard   giraffe

12. shiny   dirty   spotless   clean

Score:	Time taken:	Target met?

Target time: **12 minutes**

Take a letter away from each word to make two new words. The letter you take away should be in the same position in each word in the pair.

Example chat, flan ____cat____ , ____fan____ (remove the second letter from each word)

1. tall, till _____ , _____

2. wink, tank _____ , _____

3. gate, sown _____ , _____

In each of the sentences below, the word in capitals has three letters missing. Those three letters spell a word. Write the three-letter word in the gap.

Example My favourite toy is my teddy B _E_ _A_ _R_ . (EAR)

4. That is a pretty G __ __ __ ring.

5. The zebra has black and white S T __ __ __ E S .

6. The cat caught some M __ __ __ .

If these words were listed in alphabetical order, which word would come **first**? Write the answer on the line.

Example water milk juice cup jug _____cup_____

7. table chair paper pencil floor _____

8. fruit cheese cracker milk bread _____

9. cat mouse bird fish dog _____

Find the missing letter that completes **both** words. Write the letter on the line. Choose your answer from these letters:

d m g e p

Example bea (_m_) atch (beam and match)

10. soun (__) ance

11. dam (__) lane

12. goin (__) loat

Score:		Time taken:		Target met?	

Target time: **12 minutes**

⬇

Find the **three-letter word** hidden in each longer word. You will not need to change the letter order. Underline the word and write it on the line.

Example st<u>oo</u>p _____too_____

1. alarm _____

2. float _____

3. women _____

Find the missing letter that completes **both** words. Write the letter on the line. Choose your answer from these letters:

l n h t d m

Example bea (_m_) atch   (beam and match)

4. trai (__) ift

5. fres (__) aunt

6. trea (__) each

Underline the **two** words that contain all the same letters.

Example sip   <u>asp</u>   pit   <u>sap</u>   sit

7. tip   not   ton   toe   nut

8. pan   pun   nip   nap   pot

9. nab   net   nip   tom   ten

Underline the two words, **one** from each group, that together make one new word. The word from the first group comes first.

Example (<u>basket</u>, bag, shop)   (pin, <u>ball</u>, bin)   (basketball)

10. (garden, house, pot)   (hold, flower, traffic)

11. (step, walk, roof)   (tiles, road, ladder)

12. (deaf, blind, old)   (young, fold, sound)

Score:		Time taken:		Target met?	

Target time: **12 minutes**

Change the first word into the last word. Only change one letter at a time. You must make a new word in the middle. Write the new word on the line.

Example SIN [____BIN____] BIG

1. SUN [_____] BUG

2. LOG [_____] DON

3. BUN [_____] CUT

In each of the sentences below, the word in capitals has three letters missing. Those three letters spell a word. Write the three-letter word in the gap.

Example My favourite toy is my teddy B_E_ _A_ _R_ .   (EAR)

4. I have a pencil and a __ __ __ BER but no pen.

5. I have visited my FRI __ __ __ .

6. On a sunny day I enjoy a cold DR __ __ __ .

Underline the two words, **one** from each group, that together make one new word. The word from the first group comes first.

Example (basket, bag, shop)   (pin, ball, bin)   (basketball)

7. (nails, tooth, fingers)   (glove, clipper, paste)

8. (teeth, skin, hair)   (shampoo, brush, wash)

9. (light, bright, yellow)   (lamp, shed, house)

If these words were listed in alphabetical order, which word would come **last**? Write the answer on the line.

Example water   milk   juice   cup   jug   _____water_____

10. five   four   six   two   eight   _____

11. silly   flower   climb   string   great   _____

12. nail   hammer   spanner   screw   drill   _____

Score:		Time taken:		Target met?	

Target time: **12 minutes**

Find the next number in the sequence. Write it on the line.

Example 18   16   14   12   10   ___8___   (−2 each time)

1. 3   6   9   12   15   _____

2. 75   65   55   45   35   _____

3. 4   8   12   16   20   _____

Use the information given to answer the sum. Write your answer as a **letter**.

Example A = 2   B = 4   C = 5   D = 6   **A + B =** ___D___   (2 + 4 = 6)

4. A = 9   B = 6   C = 8   D = 2   **D + B =** _____

5. A = 3   B = 5   C = 4   D = 7   **A + C =** _____

6. A = 1   B = 9   C = 10   D = 20   **C − B =** _____

Work out the missing number. Write it on the line.

Example 5 [9] 4   2 [5] 3   7 [___10___] 3
(a + b = ?, where a is the number on the left and b is the number on the right)

7. 2 [11] 9   26 [30] 4   5 [_____] 17

8. 20 [37] 17   112 [112] 0   19 [_____] 31

9. 13 [15] 2   50 [89] 39   3 [_____] 12

Find the missing number in each equation. Write it on the line.

Example 3 + 3 = 4 + ___2___   (3 + 3 = 6 and so does 4 + 2)

10. $10 \div 2 = 3 +$ _____

11. $2 \times 6 = 13 -$ _____

12. $2 \times 2 = 1 +$ _____

Score:		Time taken:		Target met?	

Target time: **12 minutes**

Find the next letter pair in the sequence. Use the alphabet to help you. Write your answer on the line.

A B C D E F G H I J K L M N O P Q R S T U V W X Y Z

Example AB   BC   CD   DE   EF   _FG_   (+1, +1)

1. AA BB CC DD _____

2. LL MM NN OO _____

3. RR SS TT UU _____

Find the letter that completes each sentence. Use the alphabet to help you. Write your answer on the line.

A B C D E F G H I J K L M N O P Q R S T U V W X Y Z

Example **C** is to **D** as **E** is to _F_ .   (+1)

4. **X** is to **Z** as **M** is to ____ .   5. **E** is to **H** as **Q** is to ____ .   6. **W** is to **U** as **L** is to ____ .

Make a new word. Change the third pair of words in the same way as the other pairs. Write the new word on the line.

Example (bank, ban)   (cool, coo)   (dent, ____den____)
                 (take away the last letter of the first word)

7. (down, don)   (cold, cod)   (long, _____)

8. (trap, tap)   (clog, cog)   (pain, _____)

9. (four, our)   (down, own)   (fold, _____)

Match the number codes to the words. Use this to help you work out the answers to the questions. Write your answers on the lines.

CAT   TOY   COT   8 3 1   8 5 1   1 5 6

10. What is the code for **COT**? _____

11. What is the code for **TOY**? _____

12. What does the code **8 3 1** mean? _____

Score:		Time taken:		Target met?	

Verbal Reasoning Rapid Tests 2   **11**

Target time: **12 minutes**

 Work out the missing number. Write it on the line.

Example 5 [9] 4   2 [5] 3   7 [___10___] 3

(a + b = ?, where a is the number on the left and b is the number on the right)

1. 75 [100] 25   53 [76] 23   1 [_____] 72

2. 11 [6] 5   27 [20] 7   6 [_____] 0

3. 20 [8] 12   34 [11] 23   56 [_____] 49

Find the missing number in each equation. Write it on the line.

Example 3 + 3 = 4 + ___2___   (3 + 3 = 6 and so does 4 + 2)

4. 14 + 6 = 2 × _____

5. 70 ÷ 10 = 4 + _____

6. 11 × 5 = 1 + _____

Find the next number in the sequence. Write it on the line.

Example 18   16   14   12   10   ___8___   (−2 each time)

7. 4   8   12   16   _____

8. 13   24   35   46   _____

9. 10   15   20   25   _____

Use the information given to answer the sum. Write your answer as a **letter**.

Example A = 2   B = 4   C = 5   D = 6   **A + B =** ___D___   (2 + 4 = 6)

10. A = 3   B = 3   C = 9   D = 6   **D + B =** _____

11. A = 7   B = 11   C = 5   D = 4   **B − D =** _____

12. A = 10   B = 2   C = 12   D = 6   **B × D =** _____

Score:		Time taken:		Target met?	

Target time: **12 minutes**

Find the code. Use the alphabet to help you. Write your answer on the line.

A B C D E F G H I J K L M N O P Q R S T U V W X Y Z

Example If the code for **FIT** is **GJU**, what does **XBE** mean? ___WAD___

(−1 from the code to the word)

1. If the code **BSN** means **ARM**, what does the code **UPQ** mean? _____

2. If the code **BHF** means **AGE**, what does the code **BJN** mean? _____

3. If **ALL** is written in code as **DOO**, what does the code **PXG** mean? _____

Match the number codes to the words. Use this to help you work out the answers to the questions. Write your answers on the lines.

PIP   PIG   GET   356   672   353

4. What is the code for **PEG**? _____

5. What is the code for **PIT**? _____

6. What does the code **3537** mean? _____

The word in the square brackets has been made by some of the letters from the two outside words. Make a new word in the middle of the second group of words in the same way. Write the new word on the line.

Example (left [lead] read)   (jogs [___joke___] pike)

7. (rain [into] toll)   (soon [_____] cent)

8. (both [boat] heat)   (nice [_____] bone)

9. (real [read] aids)   (tuck [_____] neat)

Find the next letter pair in the sequence. Use the alphabet to help you. You might need to use a different method from the example given. Write your answer on the line.

A B C D E F G H I J K L M N O P Q R S T U V W X Y Z

Example AB   BC   CD   DE   EF   ___FG___   (+1, +1)

10. PP QQ PP QQ _____

11. AZ BY CX DW _____

12. FG GH HI IJ _____

Score:		Time taken:		Target met?	

Verbal Reasoning Rapid Tests 2

Read the following information. Work out the answers. Write your answers on the lines.

1. My father is writing letters. He writes to his father before he writes to his sister. He writes to his mother first. Who does he write to third? _____

2. A group of children are asked to line up to enter the classroom. Mary is first in the line. James is two places behind her. Shazia is second in the line. Who is third in the line? _____

3. Phil is 17 and his brother is 23. Phil's father is 25 years older than Phil.
How old is Phil's father? _____

4. Charlotte takes her dog for 2 walks every day. On how many walks does Charlotte take her dog in 1 week? _____

Choose the correct statement for each question. Circle the letter next to the **true** statement.

5. Supermarkets sell food. People go shopping in supermarkets.

   If the above statements are true, which one of the following statements must also be true?
   A   People listen to music in supermarkets.   C   Supermarkets are very noisy places.
   B   Newspapers are sold in supermarkets.   D   People can buy food in supermarkets.

6. Birds eat berries and insects. A robin is a type of bird.

   If the above statements are true, which one of the following statements must also be true?
   A   Robins eat insects and berries.   C   Birds build their nests in hedges.
   B   Robins can be seen in the garden.   D   Robins like hopping around in the snow.

Read the following questions. Work out the answers. Write your answers on the lines.

7. What is the day before Friday? _____

8. Which is the first month of the year in the UK? _____

9. If today is Friday, what day will it be tomorrow? _____

10. If it is October now, which month comes next? _____

11. My brother is 2 years older than me. I am 5. How old is my brother? _____

12. In which season is the weather coldest? _____

Score:		Time taken:		Target met?	

Read the following information. Work out the answers. Write your answers on the lines.

1. Three baby birds called Peep, Cheep and Tweet are learning to fly. Cheep jumps out of the tree first. Tweet jumps out after Cheep and Peep.
   Who is the second bird to jump? _____

2. Ajay is delivering newspapers to houses A, B and C. He goes to house B third and house C first.
   Which house does Ajay visit second? _____

3. It is midday now.
   What time was it 3 hours ago? _____

4. Billy has 19 stickers. 3 are blue, 8 are pink and 2 are green. The rest are purple.
   How many purple stickers does Billy have? _____

5. Jamie is posting letters. He posts 2 at house A, 3 at house B and 4 at house E.
   How many letters does Jamie deliver altogether? _____

6. Katie has 3 pink jumpers, 2 green hats, 4 blue pairs of trousers and 4 pink t-shirts.
   How many pink pieces of clothing does Katie have? _____

7. Sabine goes for a walk at 3.00 p.m. She gets back from her walk at 4.00 p.m.
   How long does Sabine's walk last? _____

8. It is 1.00 p.m. now. A television show I want to watch is starting in half an hour.
   What time does the television show start? _____

9. It is 5.00 p.m.
   What time was it 2 hours ago? _____

10. What time will it be in half an hour if it is 10.30 a.m. now? _____

11. Alan starts his homework at 7.00 p.m. He finishes at 8.00 p.m.
    How long does it take Alan to do his homework? _____

12. An hour ago it was 4.00 p.m.
    What time is it now? _____

Score:		Time taken:		Target met?	

⬇

▥ Read the following information. Work out the answers. Write your answers on the lines.

1. Two girls are sharing some sweets. Becky eats 3 strawberry sweets and 2 lemon sweets. Paula eats 3 lemon sweets and a raspberry sweet. How many lemon sweets do the girls eat between them? _____

2. Aaqib is drawing 10 flowers. He colours 3 flowers pink, 2 yellow and the rest he colours purple. How many purple flowers does Aaqib draw? _____

3. A house has 6 rooms. One is a bathroom, one is a kitchen and the rest are bedrooms. How many bedrooms does the house have? _____

▥ Circle the letter next to the **true** statement for each question.

4. Puppets are toys with strings attached to them. Punch and Judy are puppets.

   If the above statements are true, which one of the following statements must also be true?
   A Punch is very naughty.
   B Judy's dog steals sausages.
   C Punch and Judy are real.
   D Punch and Judy have strings attached to them.

5. Film stars are actors in films. Dev is a famous film star.

   If the above statements are true, which one of the following statements must also be true?
   A People go to the theatre to see plays.
   B Dev teaches drama in a school.
   C Cinemas show popular films.
   D Dev is an actor.

6. A person who writes stories is called an author. Alice writes lots of stories.

   If the above statements are true, which one of the following statements must also be true?
   A Alice's sister likes her stories.
   B Alice is an author.
   C Alice writes stories on a computer.
   D Stories are all true.

▥ Read the following questions. Work out the answers. Write your answers on the lines.

7. Which day comes after Tuesday? _____

8. Which month comes after January? _____

9. Which day comes before Sunday? _____

10. Sam's friend's birthday is in July. Sam's birthday is 2 months later. When is Sam's birthday? _____

11. If today is Wednesday, what day was it yesterday? _____

12. If it is spring now, which season comes next? _____

Score:		Time taken:		Target met?	

Target time: **12 minutes**

Underline the word in brackets that is **closest** in meaning to the word in capitals.

Example FALSE (real, <u>untrue</u>, halt, typical, unusual)

1. PRESENT (cake, friend, gift, party, wrap)

2. RUSH (stay, leave, rest, hurry, wait)

3. HELP (teach, learn, stuck, aid, fold)

4. START (race, begin, track, lean, car)

Choose the word that best completes the sentence. Underline the answer.

Example **Music** is to **listen** as **food** is to (touch, <u>taste</u>, drop).

5. **In** is to **out** as **happy** is to (cheerful, giggly, sad).

6. **Black** is to **white** as **old** is to (borrowed, new, second-hand).

7. **Rich** is to **poor** as **boy** is to (friends, family, girl).

8. **Clean** is to **dirty** as **night** is to (evening, day, afternoon).

Underline the word in brackets that is most **opposite** in meaning to the word in capitals.

Example BEFORE (when, then, <u>after</u>, morning, begin)

9. SHOUT (soft, angry, growl, whisper, tell)

10. FRONT (top, back, shed, stripe, garden)

11. SOFT (difficult, fur, nap, bed, hard)

Read the following information. Work out the answer. Write your answer on the line.

12. Jay has 10 red cars and 5 blue cars. He gives 6 red cars away and loses 2 blue cars. How many red cars does Jay have left? _____

Score:		Time taken:		Target met?	

Target time: **12 minutes**

1–4. For each of the words below, choose the correct group. Write its letter on the line.

W = water creature   **L** = land animal

octopus _____   camel _____

deer _____   whale _____

squirrel _____   dolphin _____

fox _____   salmon _____

In each group, three words go together and one is the odd one out. Underline the word that does **not** go with the other three.

Example pound   <u>coin</u>   hit   thump

5. piano   bow   tambourine   drums

6. sea   river   lake   beach

7. .sprint   jog   drive   walk

8. morning   yesterday   afternoon   night

Underline the word that goes best with the three words in brackets.

Example (wet, soaking, moist)   <u>damp</u>, swamp, rotten

9. (biscuit, chocolate, bun)   present, candle, cake

10. (river, lake, ocean)   boat, sea, sand

11. (pupil, headmaster, student)   teacher, book, homework

Read the following information. Work out the answer. Write your answer on the line.

12. Krisztina paints the nails on her left hand with red nail varnish and the nails on her right hand with pink nail varnish. She then paints her toenails alternating pink and red.
How many nails does she paint red? _____

Score:		Time taken:		Target met?	

Target time: **12 minutes**

In each group, three words go together and one is the odd one out. Underline the word that does **not** go with the other three.

Example pound   <u>coin</u>   hit   thump

1. mother   niece   aunt   brother

2. feathers   fur   claws   scales

3. dull   exciting   dreary   boring

4. song   melody   story   tune

Choose the word that best completes the sentence. Underline the answer.

Example **Music** is to **listen** as **food** is to (touch, <u>taste</u>, drop).

5. **Quick** is to **fast** as **large** is to (tiny, big, teeny).

6. **Small** is to **little** as **cheerful** is to (jolly, grumpy, pessimistic).

7. **Cold** is to **cool** as **hot** is to (chilly, warm, freezing).

8. **Light** is to **bright** as **dark** is to (day, dim, blazing).

Underline the two words, **one** from each group, that mean almost the **same**.

Example (typical, <u>false</u>, halt)   (unusual, real, <u>untrue</u>)

9. (break, make, bake)   (create, take, lake)

10. (mud, fall, dirty)   (rugby, bathe, filthy)

11. (hope, candle, magic)   (wish, flame, witch)

Circle the letter next to the **true** statement.

12.   Libraries have lots of books in them. Libraries lend the books to people.

If the above statements are true, which one of the following statements must also be true?
A   People can borrow books from libraries.
B   Books are very interesting.
C   People of all ages visit libraries.
D   All towns have libraries.

Score:		Time taken:		Target met?	

⬇

Add the same letter to each word pair to make two new words. Put it in the same position in each word. Choose from the letters below. Only use each letter once. Write the two new words on the lines.

e o l m g

Example ape, old _____gape_____ , _____gold_____ (add g to the start of each word)

1. fin, win _____ , _____

2. lop, hop _____ , _____

3. sow, bow _____ , _____

4. tea, sea _____ , _____

In each of the sentences below, the word in capitals has three letters missing. Those three letters spell a word. Write the three-letter word in the gap.

Example My favourite toy is my teddy B _E_ _A_ _R_ . (EAR)

5. He paid his bus F __ __ __ .

6. She flew her red __ __ __ E in the park.

7. The __ __ __ D little girl tidied her room.

8. The story was A B __ __ __ a dragon.

Rearrange the word in capitals. Use the letters to make another word that goes with the first two. Write the new word on the line.

Example high up P O T _____TOP_____

9. coffee milk E A T _____

10. point end P I T _____

11. rod hook T E N _____

Read the following information. Work out the answer. Write your answer on the line.

12. I am racing my two friends to school. I arrive at school first. Meg is third to arrive. Reuben arrives at school before Meg. Who arrives second? _____

Score:		Time taken:		Target met?	

Verbal Reasoning Rapid Tests 2 Answers

Notes for parents, tutors, teachers and other adult helpers

- **Verbal Reasoning Rapid Tests 2** is designed for seven- and eight-year-olds, but may also be suitable for some older children.

- Remove this pull-out section before giving the book to the child.

- Before the child begins work on the first test, read together the instructions on page 2, headed **What to do**. As you do so, look together at **Section 1 Test 1** and point out to the child the different elements.

- As each question type is introduced for the first time within a particular test, an example is given. Where question types recur throughout the book, the same example is provided. This is deliberate: the example will act as a useful reminder, but children will not need to work through it repeatedly from scratch.

- Make sure that the child understands how to answer the questions and that he or she has a pencil, an eraser and a sheet of rough paper. You should also ensure that the child is able to see a clock or a watch.

- Explain to the child how he or she should go about timing the test. Alternatively, you may wish to time the test yourself. When the child has finished the test, you should together work out the **Time taken** and complete the box that appears at the end of the test.

- Mark the child's work using this pull-out section, giving one mark for each correct answer unless instructed otherwise. There are a total of 12 marks available for each test. Then complete the **Score** box at the end of the test.

- The table below shows you how to mark the **Target met?** box and the **Action** notes help you to plan the next step. However, these are suggestions only. Please use your own judgement as you decide how best to proceed.

Score	Time taken	Target met?	Action
1–6	Any	Not yet	Give the child the previous book in the series. Provide help and support as needed.
7–9	Any	Not yet	Encourage the child to keep practising using the tests in this book. The child may need to repeat some tests. If so, wait a few weeks, or the child may simply remember the correct answers. Provide help and support as needed.
10–12	Over target – child took too long	Not yet	
10–12	On target – child took suggested time or less	Yes	Encourage the child to keep practising using further tests in this book, and to move on to the next book when you think this is appropriate.

- After finishing each test, the child should fill in the **Progress chart** on page 40.

- Whatever the test score, always encourage the child to have another go at the questions that he or she got wrong – without looking at the solutions. If the child's answers are still incorrect, work through these questions together. Demonstrate the correct method if necessary.

- If the child struggles with particular question types, help him or her to develop the strategies needed.

Answers

Section 1 Test 1
(page 4)

1. cheerful, joyful
2. damp, wet
3. beat, hit
4. kitchen
5. doctor
6. bark
7. right, left
8. sit, stand
9. clean, dirty
10. green (all colours)
11. car (all vehicles)
12. kangaroo (all animals)

Section 1 Test 2
(page 5)

1–3. *[score half a point for each correct answer]*
robin = B, tuna = F, cuckoo = B, owl = B,
trout = F, cod = F
4. road (the others are all found in a building)
5. field (the other words are all parts of a tree)
6. driver (the others are all forms of transport)
7. quick, slow
8. rich, poor
9. come, go
10. fast is (The train is fast.)
11. see you (How many boats can you see?)
12. milk drink (My cat likes to drink milk.)

Section 1 Test 3
(page 6)

1. smart, clever
2. finish, end
3. slim, thin
4. slow
5. right
6. puppy
7–9. *[score half a point for each correct answer]*
giraffe = A, duck = B, leopard = A,
pig = B, elephant = A, goat = B
10. chair (the others are found on plants)
11. giraffe (the others are big cats)
12. dirty (the others are all synonyms of clean)

Section 1 Test 4
(page 7)

1. all, ill (remove first letter)
2. win, tan (remove last letter)
3. ate, own (remove first letter)
4. OLD (GOLD)
5. RIP (STRIPES)
6. ICE (MICE)
7. chair
8. bread
9. bird
10. d (sound and dance)
11. p (damp and plane)
12. g (going and gloat)

Section 1 Test 5
(page 8)

1. alarm   arm
2. float   oat
3. women   men
4. l (trail and lift)
5. h (fresh and haunt)
6. t (treat and teach)
7. not, ton
8. pan, nap
9. net, ten
10. household
11. stepladder
12. blindfold

Section 1 Test 6
(page 9)

1. SUN [BUN] BUG
2. LOG [DOG] DON
3. BUN [BUT] CUT
4. RUB (RUBBER)
5. END (FRIEND)
6. INK (DRINK)
7. toothpaste
8. hairbrush
9. lighthouse
10. two
11. string
12. spanner

Section 1 Test 7
(page 10)
1. 18 (+3)
2. 25 (−10)
3. 24 (+4)
4. C (2 + 6 = 8)
5. D (3 + 4 = 7)
6. A (10 − 9 = 1)
7. 22 (a + b)
8. 50 (a + b)
9. 15 (a + b)
10. 2
11. 1
12. 3

Section 1 Test 8
(page 11)
1. EE (+1, +1)
2. PP (+1, +1)
3. VV (+1, +1)
4. O (+2)
5. T (+3)
6. J (−2)
7. log
8. pin
9. old
10. 851
11. 156
12. CAT

Section 1 Test 9
(page 12)
1. 73 (a + b)
2. 6 (a − b)
3. 7 (a − b)
4. 10
5. 3
6. 54
7. 20 (+4)
8. 57 (+11)
9. 30 (+5)
10. C (6 + 3 = 9)
11. A (11 − 4 = 7)
12. C (2 × 6 = 12)

Section 1 Test 10
(page 13)
1. TOP (−1 from the code to the word)
2. AIM (−1 from the code to the word)
3. MUD (−3 from the code to the word)
4. 376
5. 352
6. PIPE
7. once
8. nine
9. tuna
10. PP (repeating pattern)
11. EV (+1, −1)
12. JK (+1, +1)

Section 1 Test 11
(page 14)
1. his sister
2. James
3. 42
4. 14
5. D
6. A
7. Thursday
8. January
9. Saturday
10. November
11. 7
12. winter

Section 1 Test 12
(page 15)
1. Peep
2. A
3. 9 a.m./nine o'clock/09:00
4. 6
5. 9
6. 7
7. 1 hour/60 minutes
8. 1.30 p.m./half past one/13:30
9. 3.00 p.m./three o'clock/15:00
10. 11.00 a.m./eleven o'clock/11:00
11. 1 hour/60 minutes
12. 5.00 p.m./five o'clock/17:00

Answers

Section 2 Test 1
(page 16)

1. 5
2. 5
3. 4
4. D
5. D
6. B
7. Wednesday
8. February
9. Saturday
10. September
11. Tuesday
12. summer

Section 2 Test 2
(page 17)

1. gift
2. hurry
3. aid
4. begin
5. sad
6. new
7. girl
8. day
9. whisper
10. back
11. hard
12. 4

Section 2 Test 3
(page 18)

1–4. *[score half a point for each correct answer]*
octopus = W, deer = L, squirrel = L,
fox = L, camel = L, whale = W,
dolphin = W, salmon = W

5. bow (the rest are musical instruments)
6. beach (the others are all to do with water)
7. drive (this is the only one using a vehicle)
8. yesterday (the others are parts of a day)
9. cake (all baked goods)
10. sea (all large bodies of water)
11. teacher (all people at school)
12. 10

Section 2 Test 4
(page 19)

1. brother (the others are all female relatives)
2. claws (the rest are found on an animal's skin)
3. exciting (the others are synonyms of dull)
4. story (the others are to do with music)
5. big
6. jolly
7. warm
8. dim
9. make, create
10. dirty, filthy
11. hope, wish
12. A

Section 2 Test 5
(page 20)

1. fine, wine (add e)
2. loop, hoop (add o)
3. slow, blow (add l)
4. team, seam (add m)
5. ARE (FARE)
6. KIT (KITE)
7. GOO (GOOD) (accept KIN, KIND)
8. OUT (ABOUT)
9. TEA
10. TIP
11. NET
12. Reuben

Section 2 Test 6
(page 21)

1. car
2. step
3. fireman
4. electricity
5. SEA [SET] GET
6. MOW [SOW] SON
7. BAG [BIG] DIG
8. FAN [BAN] BAP
9. classroom
10. seaweed
11. hummingbird
12. 16

Schofield & Sims

Section 2 Test 7
(page 22)

1. <u>lice</u>nce   lice
2. leng<u>then</u>   then
3. <u>trap</u>ped   trap
4. <u>show</u>n   show
5. s (press and shear)
6. d (rapid and dress)
7. e (stole and earn)
8. suitcase
9. lightbulb
10. toothpick
11. armpit
12. 2

Section 2 Test 8
(page 23)

1. 66 (+11)
2. 24 (+3)
3. 12 (−5)
4. 60 (+10)
5. D (20 ÷ 10 = 2)
6. A (5 × 3 = 15)
7. A (2 × 5 = 10)
8. B (8 + 9 = 17)
9. 61 (a − b)
10. 0 (a − b)
11. 7 (a ÷ b)
12. pears

Section 2 Test 9
(page 24)

1. cat
2. tall
3. win
4. sort
5. 935
6. 394
7. 1993
8. WOOD
9. AR (same, +1)
10. IS (+2, +2)
11. XU (+1, +2, +3, +4)
12. kiwis

Section 2 Test 10
(page 25)

1. 50 (a + b)
2. 50 (a + b)
3. 11 (a ÷ b)
4. 12 (a − b)
5. 9
6. 2
7. 1
8. A (28 − 9 = 19)
9. C (100 ÷ 10 = 10)
10. A (18 ÷ 2 = 9)
11. D (9 + 5 = 14)
12. B

Section 2 Test 11
(page 26)

1. 5
2. 1
3. 2
4. 1
5. 19 (+4)
6. 12 (−3)
7. 16 (+4)
8. 1 (÷10)
9. C (30 ÷ 5 = 6)
10. D (22 − 8 = 14)
11. D (24 ÷ 2 = 12)
12. Friday

Section 2 Test 12
(page 27)

1. keep
2. king
3. mile
4. dent
5. NEW (−1 from the code to the word)
6. LCY (+2 from the word to the code)
7. MBC (+1 from the word to the code)
8. OLH (+3 from the word to the code)
9. V (+3)
10. D (−3)
11. G (+5)
12. 7

Answers

Section 3 Test 1
(page 28)

1–4. *[score half a point for each correct answer]*
hood = H, slipper = F, helmet = H,
bonnet = H, sandal = F, cap = H,
trainer = F, boot = F
5. 16 (+2)
6. 22 (−11)
7. 16 (×2)
8. 51 (−10)
9. staircase
10. graveyard
11. woodland
12. 2

Section 3 Test 2
(page 29)

1. 3 (a ÷ b)
2. 30 (a + b)
3. 12 (a × b)
4. 21 (a − b)
5. BUS
6. CUT
7. TON
8. NAP
9. HEN (WHEN)
10. HER (OTHER)
11. BIT (BITE)
12. A

Section 3 Test 3
(page 30)

1. sea, pea (remove last letter)
2. cut, hut (remove third letter)
3. tap, fat (remove second letter)
4. lot, low (remove first letter)
5. 2
6. 8
7. 6
8. 4
9. 415
10. 724
11. POOL
12. Beth

Section 3 Test 4
(page 31)

1. mule
2. daft
3. cousin
4. sell
5. M (−5)
6. NO (+2, +2)
7. EG (+3, +3)
8. TU (+1, +1)
9. A (5 × 9 = 45)
10. B (18 + 12 = 30)
11. D (60 ÷ 10 = 6)
12. 16

Section 3 Test 5
(page 32)

1. the feeds (The zookeeper feeds the
   elephants.)
2. my is (Here is my house.)
3. the watched (The boy watched the match.)
4. dresses wear (Girls often wear dresses.)
5. c (music and chalk)
6. f (sniff and fudge)
7. e (dodge and early)
8. l (snarl and lever)
9. VG (−1, −1)
10. IH (+2, same)
11. SS (repeating pattern)
12. Anya

Section 3 Test 6
(page 33)

1. D (5 × 8 = 40)
2. C (24 − 12 = 12)
3. B (11 × 2 = 22)
4. A (25 ÷ 5 = 5)
5. BAR (−2 from the code to the word)
6. LMU (−2 from the word to the code)
7. GJY (+1 from the word to the code)
8. love, adore
9. happy, glad
10. tasty, delicious
11. munch, chew
12. 5

Section 3 Test 7
(page 34)

1. waterfall
2. rainbow
3. farmyard
4. k (spook and king)
5. d (greed and dined)
6. p (group and plant)
7. n (drain and near)
8. imprint   imp
9. shell   she
10. neighbour   our
11. shipped   hip
12. 4 May

Section 3 Test 8
(page 35)

1. 60 (a × b)
2. 4 (a ÷ b)
3. 23 (a + b)
4. 12 (a − b)
5. best, worst
6. lift, drop
7. throw, catch
8. same, different
9. GAS [GAP] RAP
10. BOAT [MOAT] MOAN
11. FLIP [SLIP] SLIM
12. D

Section 3 Test 9
(page 36)

1. gain
2. nap
3. drop
4. pun
5. terrifying (all synonyms for frightening)
6. glass (all types of materials)
7. smell (all senses)
8. right (all directions)
9. nice
10. sort
11. well
12. Raj's shop

Section 3 Test 10
(page 37)

1. BC (−2, −2)
2. UW (+3, +3)
3. DE (+2, +2)
4. NL (+3, +3)
5. clothes (the others are types of furniture)
6. glove (the others are types of footwear)
7. whisper (the others are loud noises)
8. WT (same, +1)
9. OK (+2, −3)
10. QK (−1, −1)
11. NO (+3, +3)
12. yes

Section 3 Test 11
(page 38)

1. rabbit
2. aunt
3. slither
4. rich
5. 10 (−5)
6. 9 (+2)
7. 3 (÷2)
8. 21 (+4)
9. sent
10. fire
11. rage
12. 30 minutes/half an hour

Section 3 Test 12
(page 39)

1. 9
2. 10
3. 10
4. 6
5. 715
6. 7519
7. AJAR
8. run, walk
9. laugh, cry
10. break, fix
11. stay, leave
12. C

This book of answers is a pull-out section from
Verbal Reasoning Rapid Tests 2

Published by **Schofield & Sims Ltd**,
7 Mariner Court, Wakefield, West Yorkshire WF4 3FL, UK
Telephone 01484 607080
www.schofieldandsims.co.uk

First published in 2014
This edition copyright © Schofield & Sims Ltd, 2018
Fourth impression 2021

Author: **Siân Goodspeed**. Siân Goodspeed has asserted her moral right under the Copyright, Designs and Patents Act, 1988, to be identified as the author of this work.

British Library Cataloguing in Publication Data
A catalogue record for this book is available from the British Library.

Commissioned by **Carolyn Richardson Publishing Services**

Design by **Oxford Designers & Illustrators**
Printed in the UK by **Page Bros (Norwich) Ltd**

ISBN 978 07217 1451 6

Target time: **12 minutes**

If these words were listed in alphabetical order, which word would come **third**? Write the answer on the line.

Example water   juice   milk   cup   jug _____juice_____

1. car   van   lorry   boat   barge _____

2. walk   run   waddle   jog   step _____

3. farmer   grocer   fireman   doctor   nurse _____

4. air   water   fire   earth   electricity _____

Change the first word into the last word. Only change **one** letter at a time. You must make a new word in the middle. Write the new word on the line.

Example SIN [_____BIN_____] BIG

5. SEA [_____] GET

6. MOW [_____] SON

7. BAG [_____] DIG

8. FAN [_____] BAP

Underline the two words, **one** from each group, that together make one new word. The word from the first group comes first.

Example (basket, bag, shop)   (pin, ball, bin)   (basketball)

9. (class, rules, teacher)   (school, pupil, room)

10. (beach, sea, sand)   (wave, weed, flag)

11. (singing, humming, crying)   (fish, mouse, bird)

Read the following information. Work out the answer. Write your answer on the line.

12. Nisha plays tennis on Saturdays. In the morning she has 14 tennis balls.
She loses 3 balls. Her friend gives her 5 balls.
How many tennis balls does Nisha have at the end of the day? _____

Score:		Time taken:		Target met?	

Find the **four-letter word** hidden in each longer word. You will not need to change the letter order. Underline the word and write it on the line.

Example <u>train</u> _____<u>rain</u>_____

1. licence _____

2. lengthen _____

3. trapped _____

4. shown _____

Find the missing letter that completes **both** words. Write the letter on the line. Choose your answer from these letters:

a d m s e f

Example bea (_m_) atch   (beam and match)

5. pres (___) hear

6. rapi (___) ress

7. stol (___) arn

Underline the two words, **one** from each group, that together make one new word. The word from the first group comes first.

Example (<u>basket</u>, bag, shop)   (pin, <u>ball</u>, bin)   (basketball)

8. (suit, tie, jacket)   (file, case, link)

9. (light, move, hose)   (bulb, flower, pot)

10. (teeth, tooth, mouth)   (scratch, bite, pick)

11. (body, leg, arm)   (mine, pit, shirt)

Read the following information. Work out the answer. Write your answer on the line.

12. Frank's friends are called Bill, Rebecca, Bryony and Amir. Frank's father is called Brian. How many of Frank's friends have a name beginning with B? _____

Score:		Time taken:		Target met?	

Target time: **12 minutes**

Find the next number in the sequence. Write it on the line.

Example   18   16   14   12   10   __8__   (−2 each time)

1. 22   33   44   55   _____

2. 12   15   18   21   _____

3. 32   27   22   17   _____

4. 20   30   40   50   _____

Use the information given to answer the sum. Write your answer as a **letter**.

Example A = 2   B = 4   C = 5   D = 6   **A + B =** __D__   (2 + 4 = 6)

5. A = 20   B = 10   C = 25   D = 2   **A ÷ B =** _____

6. A = 15   B = 10   C = 3   D = 5   **D × C =** _____

7. A = 10   B = 2   C = 17   D = 5   **B × D =** _____

8. A = 8   B = 17   C = 19   D = 9   **A + D =** _____

Work out the missing number. Write it on the line.

Example 5 [9] 4   2 [5] 3   7 [__10__] 3

(a + b = ?, where a is the number on the left and b is the number on the right)

9. 14 [8] 6   59 [49] 10   77 [_____] 16

10. 63 [50] 13   24 [17] 7   8 [_____] 8

11. 80 [8] 10   90 [9] 10   70 [_____] 10

Read the following information. Work out the answer. Write your answer on the line.

12. My mother buys some apples, bananas and pears. She buys the bananas after she buys the pears, but before she buys the apples.
Which does she buy first: apples, bananas or pears? _____

Score:	Time taken:	Target met?

Verbal Reasoning Rapid Tests 2

Make a new word. Change the third pair of words in the same way as the other pairs. Write the new word on the line.

Example (bank, ban)   (cool, coo)   (dent, _____den_____)
(take away the last letter of the first word)

1. (knit, kit)   (snip, sip)   (coat, _____)

2. (learn, earn)   (steam, team)   (stall, _____)

3. (town, tow)   (took, too)   (wing, _____)

4. (stack, sack)   (smock, sock)   (snort, _____)

Match the number codes to the words. Use this to help you work out the answers to the questions. Write your answers on the lines.

OWL   OUT   DUO   529   913   924

5. What is the code for **OLD**? _____

6. What is the code for **LOT**? _____

7. What is the code for **WOOL**? _____

8. What does the code **1995** mean? _____

Find the next letter pair in the sequence. Use the alphabet to help you. Write your answer on the line.

A B C D E F G H I J K L M N O P Q R S T U V W X Y Z

Example AB   BC   CD   DE   EF   _FG_   (+1, +1)

9. AN   AO   AP   AQ   _____

10. AK   CM   EO   GQ   _____

11. NK   OL   QN   TQ   _____

Read the following information. Work out the answer. Write your answer on the line.

12. Jenny only likes red fruits. Josef only likes yellow and orange fruits. They share a fruit salad that is made of strawberries, oranges, bananas, kiwis, pineapple and cherries.
Which of the fruits in the salad do neither of them eat? _____

Score:	Time taken:	Target met?

Target time: **12 minutes**

Work out the missing number. Write it on the line.

Example 5 [9] 4   2 [5] 3   7 [___10___] 3

(a + b = ?, where a is the number on the left and b is the number on the right)

1. 20 [50] 30   10 [50] 40   15 [_____] 35

2. 49 [50] 1   48 [50] 2   47 [_____] 3

3. 15 [3] 5   25 [5] 5   55 [_____] 5

4. 19 [10] 9   18 [9] 9   21 [_____] 9

Find the missing number in each equation. Write it on the line.

Example 3 + 3 = 4 + ___2___   (3 + 3 = 6 and so does 4 + 2)

5. 24 − 6 = 2 × _____

6. 60 ÷ 5 = 6 × _____

7. 7 × 2 = 13 + _____

Use the information given to answer the sum. Write your answer as a **letter**.

Example A = 2   B = 4   C = 5   D = 6   **A + B =** ___D___   (2 + 4 = 6)

8. A = 19   B = 28   C = 36   D = 9   **B − D =** _____

9. A = 20   B = 100   C = 10   D = 5   **B ÷ C =** _____

10. A = 9   B = 2   C = 22   D = 18   **D ÷ B =** _____

11. A = 9   B = 5   C = 21   D = 14   **A + B =** _____

Circle the letter next to the **true** statement.

12. Father always wears his glasses to read books. Father is reading a book now.

If the above statements are true, which one of the following statements must also be true?

A Reading books is bad for your eyes.

B Father is wearing his glasses now.

C The television is boring.

D Father needs to clean his glasses.

Score:		Time taken:		Target met?	

Target time: **12 minutes**

Find the missing number in each equation. Write it on the line.

Example 3 + 3 = 4 + ___2___   (3 + 3 = 6 and so does 4 + 2)

1. 5 × 5 = 20 + _____

2. 7 × 5 = 36 − _____

3. 50 ÷ 10 = 3 + _____

4. 20 ÷ 5 = 3 + _____

Find the next number in the sequence. Write it on the line.

Example 18   16   14   12   10   ___8___   (−2 each time)

5. 3   7   11   15   _____

6. 24   21   18   15   _____

7. 0   4   8   12   _____

8. 10 000   1000   100   10   _____

Use the information given to answer the sum. Write your answer as a **letter**.

Example A = 2   B = 4   C = 5   D = 6   **A + B =** ___D___   (2 + 4 = 6)

9. A = 30   B = 5   C = 6   D = 40   **A ÷ B =** _____

10. A = 8   B = 22   C = 32   D = 14   **B − A =** _____

11. A = 30   B = 2   C = 24   D = 12   **C ÷ B =** _____

Read the following question. Work out the answer. Write your answer on the line.

12. What is the day after Thursday? _____

Score:		Time taken:		Target met?	

Target time: **12 minutes**

The word in square brackets has been made by some of the letters from the two outside words. Make a new word in the middle of the second group of words in the same way. Write the new word on the line.

Example (left [lead] read)   (jogs [_____joke_____] pike)

1. (bride [desk] skip)   (stake [_____] epic)

2. (slat [slug] smug)   (kite [_____] hung)

3. (hilt [hire] reap)   (mint [_____] left)

4. (west [word] cord)   (dice [_____] rent)

Find the code. Use the alphabet to help you. Write your answer on the line.

A B C D E F G H I J K L M N O P Q R S T U V W X Y Z

Example If the code for **FIT** is **GJU**, what does **XBE** mean?   _____WAD_____

(−1 from the code to the word)

5. If the code **BOU** means **ANT**, what does the code **OFX** mean? _____

6. If the code for **BED** is **DGF**, what is the code for **JAW**? _____

7. If the code for **HOT** is **IPU**, what is the code for **LAB**? _____

8. If the code for **BOW** is **ERZ**, what is the code for **LIE**? _____

Find the letter that completes each sentence. Use the alphabet to help you. Write your answer on the line.

A B C D E F G H I J K L M N O P Q R S T U V W X Y Z

Example **C** is to **D** as **E** is to ___F___ .   (+1)

9. **V** is to **Y** as **S** is to _____ .

10. **Q** is to **N** as **G** is to _____ .

11. **H** is to **M** as **B** is to _____ .

Read the following information. Work out the answer. Write your answer on the line.

12. Chen is 14. Her brother is half her age. How old is Chen's brother? _____

Score:		Time taken:		Target met?	

Target time: **12 minutes**

1–4. For each of the words below, choose the correct group. Write its letter on the line.

F = foot   **H** = head

hood _____   sandal _____

slipper _____   cap _____

helmet _____   trainer _____

bonnet _____   boot _____

Find the next number in the sequence. Write it on the line.

Example 18   16   14   12   10   ___8___   (−2 each time)

5. 8   10   12   14   _____

6. 66   55   44   33   _____

7. 1   2   4   8   _____

8. 91   81   71   61   _____

Underline the two words, **one** from each group, that together make one new word. The word from the first group comes first.

Example (<u>basket</u>, bag, shop)   (pin, <u>ball</u>, bin)   (basketball)

9. (step, climb, stair)   (file, case, need)

10. (grave, serious, mood)   (garden, yard, church)

11. (forest, wood, tree)   (land, country, place)

Read the following information. Work out the answer. Write your answer on the line.

12. Patrick has 3 pet parrots. One has blue, red and yellow feathers. One has green, yellow and blue feathers. The last parrot has red, blue and green feathers.
How many parrots have red feathers? _____

Score:		Time taken:		Target met?	

Target time: **12 minutes**

Work out the missing number. Write it on the line.

Example 5 [9] 4   2 [5] 3   7 [___10___] 3

(a + b = ?, where a is the number on the left and b is the number on the right)

1. 45 [9] 5   55 [11] 5   15 [_____] 5

2. 12 [23] 11   15 [40] 25   17 [_____] 13

3. 4 [8] 2   2 [4] 2   6 [_____] 2

4. 22 [19] 3   35 [30] 5   27 [_____] 6

Rearrange the capital letters to make a new word so that the sentence makes sense. Write the new word on the line.

Example The **N M A** put on his hat.   ___MAN___

5. Gran caught the **U S B**. _____

6. Dad **T U C** the lawn. _____

7. The elephant weighed a **N O T**. _____

8. The dog curled up for a **P N A**. _____

In each of the sentences below, the word in capitals has three letters missing. Those three letters spell a word. Write the three-letter word in the gap.

Example My favourite toy is my teddy B _E_ _A_ _R_. (EAR)

9. W __ __ __ are we going?

10. Where is my OT__ __ __ shoe?

11. Be careful, the dog might __ __ __ E you!

Circle the letter next to the **true** statement.

12.   Rock pools are found at the seaside. Crabs live in rock pools.

If the above statements are true, which one of the following statements must also be true?

A Crabs are found at the seaside.   C Seaweed grows on rocks.

B There is a lot of sand on a beach.   D Crabs walk sideways.

Score:		Time taken:		Target met?	

Target time: **12 minutes**

Take a letter away from each word to make two new words. The letter you take away should be in the same position in each word in the pair.

Example chat, film _____cat_____ , _____fan_____ (remove the second letter from each word)

1. seal, peal _____ , _____

2. curt, hurt _____ , _____

3. trap, flat _____ , _____

4. clot, flow _____ , _____

Find the missing number in each equation. Write it on the line.

Example 3 + 3 = 4 + ___2___ (3 + 3 = 6 and so does 4 + 2)

5. 80 ÷ 10 = 4 × _____

6. 7 × 4 = 20 + _____

7. 2 × 12 = 18 + _____

8. 50 ÷ 5 = 14 − _____

Match the number codes to the words. Use this to help you work out the answers to the questions. Write your answers on the lines.

DOG GAP LAD 324 513 725

9. What is the code for **POD**? _____

10. What is the code for **LAP**? _____

11. What does the code **4117** mean? _____

Read the following information. Work out the answer. Write your answer on the line.

12. Seona is driving a car. Grace is sitting on Seona's left. Jill is sitting behind Seona. Beth is sitting behind Grace.
   Who is sitting on Jill's left? _____

Score:		Time taken:		Target met?	

Target time: 12 minutes

If these words were listed in alphabetical order, which word would come **third**? Write the answer on the line.

Example water   milk   juice   cup   jug   ____juice____

1. zebra   horse   pony   donkey   mule   _____

2. kind   clever   cruel   daft   friendly   _____

3. uncle   aunt   cousin   brother   daughter   _____

4. market   shop   stall   buy   sell   _____

Find the letter or letter pair that completes each sentence. Use the alphabet to help you. Write your answer on the line.

A B C D E F G H I J K L M N O P Q R S T U V W X Y Z

Example **CE** is to **DF** as **EG** is to __FH__.   (+1, +1)

5. **X** is to **S** as **R** is to _____ .

6. **CD** is to **EF** as **LM** is to _____ .

7. **DF** is to **GI** as **BD** is to _____ .

8. **OP** is to **PQ** as **ST** is to _____ .

Use the information given to answer the sum. Write your answer as a **letter**.

Example A = 2   B = 4   C = 5   D = 6   **A + B =** __D__   (2 + 4 = 6)

9. A = 45   B = 5   C = 80   D = 9   **B × D =** _____

10. A = 12   B = 30   C = 20   D = 18   **D + A =** _____

11. A = 50   B = 10   C = 60   D = 6   **C ÷ B =** _____

Read the following information. Work out the answer. Write your answer on the line.

12. Jess and Abdul are bird-watching. Jess sees 2 pigeons, 3 doves and a robin. Abdul sees 7 sparrows and 3 blackbirds. How many birds do Jess and Abdul spot altogether? _____

Score:		Time taken:		Target met?	

⬇

Two words in each sentence must change places so that the sentence makes sense. Underline the words.

Example I <u>a</u> <u>need</u> nap.   (I need a nap.)

1. The zookeeper the feeds elephants.

2. Here my is house.

3. The boy the watched match.

4. Girls often dresses wear.

Find the missing letter that completes **both** words. Write the letter on the line. Choose your answer from these letters:

j e f c l m

Example bea (_m_) atch   (beam and match)

5. musi (__) halk

6. snif (__) udge

7. dodg (__) arly

8. snar (__) ever

Find the next letter pair in the sequence. Use the alphabet to help you. You might need to use a different method from the example given. Write your answer on the line.

A B C D E F G H I J K L M N O P Q R S T U V W X Y Z

Example AB   BC   CD   DE   EF   <u>FG</u>   (+1, +1)

9. ZK   YJ   XI   WH   _____

10. AH   CH   EH   GH   _____

11. SS   TT   SS   TT   _____

Read the following information. Work out the answer. Write your answer on the line.

12. Four children are waiting in the line for the ice cream van. James is second in the line. Miles is at the back of the line. Anya is in front of Miles. Ayesha is at the front of the line. Who is third in the line? _____

Score:		Time taken:		Target met?	

Target time: **12 minutes**

Use the information given to answer the sum. Write your answer as a **letter**.

Example A = 2   B = 4   C = 5   D = 6   **A + B =** ___D___   (2 + 4 = 6)

1. A = 5   B = 60   C = 8   D = 40   **A × C =** _____

2. A = 24   B = 30   C = 12   D = 2   **A − C =** _____

3. A = 2   B = 22   C = 11   D = 20   **C × A =** _____

4. A = 5   B = 30   C = 15   D = 25   **D ÷ A =** _____

Find the code. Use the alphabet to help you. Write your answer on the line.

A B C D E F G H I J K L M N O P Q R S T U V W X Y Z

Example If the code for **FIT** is **GJU**, what does **XBE** mean?   ___WAD___

(−1 from the code to the word)

5. If the code for **AXE** is **CZG**, what does the code **DCT** mean? _____

6. If **ICE** is written in code as **GAC**, what is the code for **NOW**? _____

7. If the code for **GAP** is **HBQ**, what is the code for **FIX**? _____

Underline the pair of words that mean almost the **same**.

Example (typical, unusual)   (halt, real)   (false, untrue)

8. (heart, kiss)   (love, adore)   (dine, card)

9. (happy, glad)   (smile, trick)   (dream, nap)

10. (meal, aroma)   (stir, cook)   (tasty, delicious)

11. (swallow, squeeze)   (spit, rude)   (munch, chew)

Read the following information. Work out the answer. Write your answer on the line.

12. Nathan does the washing-up every day except Friday. On Mondays and Wednesdays he wears pink rubber gloves. On Tuesdays, Thursdays and Saturdays he wears blue rubber gloves. On Sundays he doesn't wear any gloves. On how many days of the week does Nathan wear gloves to do the washing-up? _____

Score:		Time taken:		Target met?	

Verbal Reasoning Rapid Tests 2   33

⬇

Underline the two words, **one** from each group, that together make one new word. The word from the first group comes first.

Example (<u>basket</u>, bag, shop)   (pin, <u>ball</u>, bin)   (basketball)

1. (river, rush, water)   (flow, fall, drop)

2. (rain, lake, cloud)   (arrow, bow, shoot)

3. (farm, man, bird)   (place, chair, yard)

Find the missing letter that completes **both** words. Write the letter on the line. Choose your answer from these letters:

d k n p c m

Example bea (<u>m</u>) atch   (beam and match)

4. spoo (__) ing

5. gree (__) ined

6. grou (__) lant

7. drai (__) ear

Find the **three-letter word** hidden in each longer word. You will not need to change the letter order. Underline the word and write it on the line.

Example <u>sto</u>op _____too_____

8. imprint _____

9. shell _____

10. neighbour _____

11. shipped _____

Read the following question. Work out the answer. Write your answer on the line.

12. If it is 3 May today, what will the date be tomorrow? _____

Score:		Time taken:		Target met?	

Target time: **12 minutes**

Work out the missing number. Write it on the line.

Example 5 [9] 4   2 [5] 3   7 [___10___] 3

(a + b = ?, where a is the number on the left and b is the number on the right)

1. 2 [10] 5   4 [20] 5   12 [_____] 5

2. 50 [5] 10   60 [6] 10   40 [_____] 10

3. 16 [21] 5   10 [20] 10   14 [_____] 9

4. 17 [8] 9   8 [5] 3   24 [_____] 12

Underline the two words, **one** from each group, that are most **opposite** in meaning.

Example (after, morning, begin)   (before, then, when)

5. (naughty, lost, best)   (bad, worst, prize)

6. (through, lift, give)   (drop, slide, bat)

7. (net, throw, hit)   (trick, ball, catch)

8. (same, some, nice)   (like, different, too)

Change the first word into the last word. Only change **one** letter at a time. You must make a new word in the middle. Write the new word on the line.

Example SIN [_____BIN_____] BIG

9. GAS [_____] RAP

10. BOAT [_____] MOAN

11. FLIP [_____] SLIM

Circle the letter next to the **true** statement.

12.   Ostriches and penguins are birds. Ostriches and penguins cannot fly.

If the above statements are true, which one of the following statements must also be true?

A Ostriches lay eggs.

B Penguins are friendly with other birds.

C Ostriches come from Africa.

D Not all birds are able to fly.

Score:		Time taken:		Target met?	

Target time: **12 minutes**

Make a new word. Change the third pair of words in the same way as the other pairs. Write the new word on the line.

Example (bank, ban) (cool, coo) (dent, ___den___)

(take away the last letter of the first word)

1. (sling, sing) (skill, sill) (grain, _____)

2. (skip, kip) (what, hat) (snap, _____)

3. (cheat, chat) (cheap, chap) (droop, _____)

4. (till, ill) (heel, eel) (spun, _____)

Underline the word that goes best with the three words in brackets.

Example (wet, soaking, moist) <u>damp</u>, swamp, rotten

5. (frightening, scary, petrifying) terrifying, boring, silly

6. (paper, plastic, brick) drain, glass, salt

7. (listen, taste, touch) cheese, music, smell

8. (up, down, left) write, right, forgot

Choose the word that best completes the sentence. Underline the answer.

Example **Music** is to **listen** as **food** is to (touch, <u>taste</u>, drop).

9. **Mean** is to **nasty** as **kind** is to (arrogant, smiley, nice).

10. **Beautiful** is to **pretty** as **organise** is to (type, sort, play).

11. **Sick** is to **ill** as **healthy** is to (poorly, sad, well).

Read the following information. Work out the answer. Write your answer on the line.

12. Raj works in a shop. He sells chocolate bars, magazines and pens.
Leah works in a different shop. She sells cakes, flowers and sweets.
Bella wants to buy a pen. Whose shop must she go to? _____

Score:		Time taken:		Target met?	

Schofield & Sims

Target time: **12 minutes**

Find the letter pair that completes each sentence. Use the alphabet to help you. Write your answer on the line.

A B C D E F G H I J K L M N O P Q R S T U V W X Y Z

Example **CE** is to **DF** as **EG** is to __FH__ .   (+1, +1)

1. **QR** is to **OP** as **DE** is to _____ .

2. **JL** is to **MO** as **RT** is to _____ .

3. **VW** is to **XY** as **BC** is to _____ .

4. **SQ** is to **VT** as **KI** is to _____ .

In each group, three words go together and one is the odd one out. Underline the word that does **not** go with the other three.

Example pound   <u>coin</u>   hit   thump

5. shelf   clothes   cupboard   wardrobe

6. boot   slipper   glove   sandal

7. shout   whisper   scream   yell

Find the next letter pair in the sequence. Use the alphabet to help you. Write your answer on the line.

A B C D E F G H I J K L M N O P Q R S T U V W X Y Z

Example AB   BC   CD   DE   EF   __FG__   (+1, +1)

8. WP   WQ   WR   WS   _____

9. GW   IT   KQ   MN   _____

10. UO   TN   SM   RL   _____

11. BC   EF   HI   KL   _____

Read the following information. Work out the answer. Write your answer on the line.

12. Liam is counting his money. He has three 20 pence pieces and two 50 pence pieces. Does he have enough money to buy an ice cream for £1.50? _____

Score:		Time taken:		Target met?	

Verbal Reasoning Rapid Tests 2

Target time: **12 minutes**

Choose the word that best completes the sentence. Underline the answer.

Example Music is to **listen** as **food** is to (touch, <u>taste</u>, drop).

1. **House** is to **people** as **hutch** is to (straw, horse, rabbit).

2. **King** is to **queen** as **uncle** is to (brother, aunt, sister).

3. **Leopard** is to **run** as **snake** is to (hop, slither, skip).

4. **Like** is to **dislike** as **poor** is to (rich, unwell, bucket).

Find the next number in the sequence. Write it on the line.

Example 18   16   14   12   10   ___8___   (−2 each time)

5. 30   25   20   15   _____

6. 1   3   5   7   _____

7. 48   24   12   6   _____

8. 5   9   13   17   _____

The word in square brackets has been made by some of the letters from the two outside words. Make a new word in the middle of the second group of words in the same way. Write the new word on the line.

Example (left [lead] read)   (j<u>o</u>gs [___joke___] pi<u>ke</u>)

9. (game [gale] bale)   (seek [_____] font)

10. (fold [four] sure)   (fins [_____] bred)

11. (spit [pink] bunk)   (brat [_____] edge)

Read the following information. Work out the answer. Write your answer on the line.

12. Leon starts cooking his dinner at 7.00 p.m. He sits down to eat at 7.30 p.m. How long does it take him to cook his dinner? _____

Score:		Time taken:		Target met?	

Target time: **12 minutes**

Find the missing number in each equation. Write it on the line.

Example 3 + 3 = 4 + ___2___   (3 + 3 = 6 and so does 4 + 2)

1. 100 ÷ 10 = 19 − _____

2. 7 × 10 = 60 + _____

3. 27 − 5 = 12 + _____

4. 14 + 9 = 29 − _____

Match the number codes to the words. Use this to help you work out the answers to the questions. Write your answers on the lines.

JAW   PAW   JAR   9 1 7   6 1 5   6 1 7

5. What is the code for **WAR**? _____

6. What is the code for **WRAP**? _____

7. What does the code **1 6 1 5** mean? _____

Underline the pair of words that are most **opposite** in meaning.

Example (begin, when)   (morning, then)   (after, before)

8. (foot, slipper)   (run, walk)   (bend, lean)

9. (funny, film)   (dip, hop)   (laugh, cry)

10. (plate, dinner)   (glass, trip)   (break, fix)

11. (stay, leave)   (step, wait)   (holiday, home)

Circle the letter next to the **true** statement.

12.   People use telephones to talk to other people. Ed is using a telephone.

If the above statements are true, which one of the following statements must also be true?

A Ed is ordering a pizza.

B Ed cannot hear the person he is talking to.

C Ed is talking to somebody.

D Ed will be using the telephone for a long time.

Score:		Time taken:		Target met?	

Progress chart

Write the score (out of 12) for each test in the box provided on the right of the graph.
Then colour in the row next to the box to represent this score.

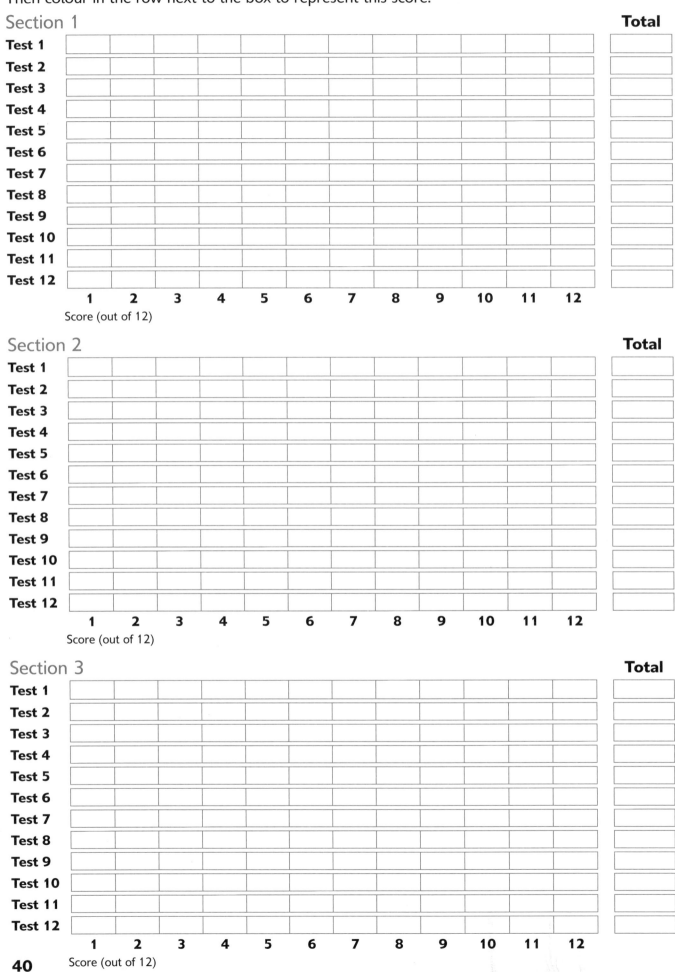

Section 1   **Total**

Test 1
Test 2
Test 3
Test 4
Test 5
Test 6
Test 7
Test 8
Test 9
Test 10
Test 11
Test 12

    1   2   3   4   5   6   7   8   9 10 11 12
Score (out of 12)

Section 2   **Total**

Test 1
Test 2
Test 3
Test 4
Test 5
Test 6
Test 7
Test 8
Test 9
Test 10
Test 11
Test 12

    1   2   3   4   5   6   7   8   9 10 11 12
Score (out of 12)

Section 3   **Total**

Test 1
Test 2
Test 3
Test 4
Test 5
Test 6
Test 7
Test 8
Test 9
Test 10
Test 11
Test 12

    1   2   3   4   5   6   7   8   9 10 11 12
40   Score (out of 12)